OUR FAMILY STORY

A HISTORY OF OUR FAMILY

LONGMEADOW
PRESS

Our Family Story
Originated by Julie Hausner

Published exclusively by
Longmeadow Press
201 High Ridge Road
PO Box 10218
Stamford, CT 06904

ISBN: 0-681-40185-0

Manufactured in the United States of America.

Picture Credits: Bettman Archive & Dover Publication, *Handbook of Early Advertising Art*

Our
Family
Story

This Book is
Lovingly Dedicated To:

_____

This Record was compiled by:

_____

_____

and started on _____

A family record is more than names, dates and places. It is about people—what they did, the why and the how. This book is designed so you can record forever, in one volume, the history of your family and your ancestors.

There are sections where you can enter the origins of your family: where your ancestors came from and when, what happened to them, and the things they did. You will also be able to record, perhaps for the first time, stories about members of your family that have been handed down from preceding generations. There are other sections devoted to family photographs, traditions and such memorable events as weddings and reunions. And there is a most important "how to" section that will help

you trace your family's history: where to write to obtain records, what information to include in such inquiries, and what institutions are available to you for further assistance (such as libraries and bookstores that specialize in genealogy information).

From the birth of a great, great grandparent to the birth of the newest baby in your family, this book provides a wonderful opportunity to gather together in one place all the interesting and unusual aspects of your family's history. When complete, it will be a storehouse of treasured information, achievements and memories—a permanent record of your family which is unique and not like any other.

CONTENTS

Our Family

This Certifies that

_____

And

_____

Were United in Holy Matrimony

Place of Ceremony_____

City_____ **State**_____

Month_____ **Day**_____ **Year**_____

Married by_____

_____

4

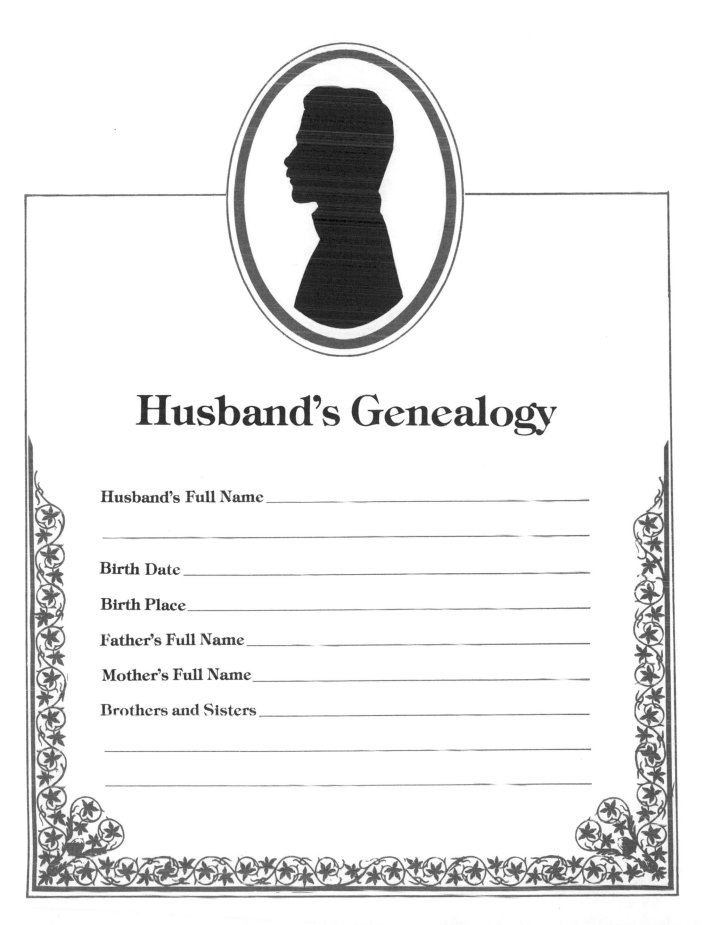

Husband's Genealogy

Husband's Full Name _____

_____

Birth Date _____

Birth Place _____

Father's Full Name _____

Mother's Full Name _____

Brothers and Sisters _____

_____

_____

Wife's Genealogy

Wife's Full Name _____

_____

Birth Date _____

Birth Place _____

Father's Full Name _____

Mother's Full Name _____

Brothers and Sisters _____

_____

_____

Our Children

Full Name	Place of Birth	Date of Birth

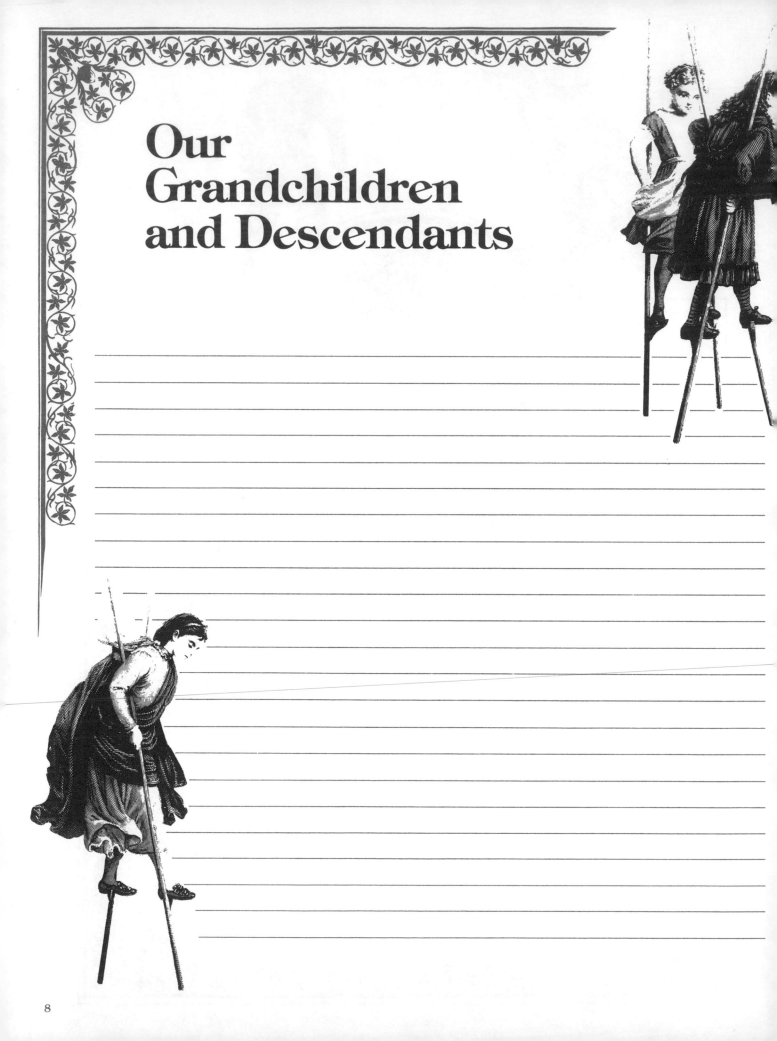

Our Grandchildren and Descendants

Our Family Tree

HUSBAND'S FULL NAME _____

WIFE'S FULL NAME _____

DATE OF MARRIAGE _____ PLACE OF MARRIAGE _____

OUR CHILDREN

_____

_____

_____

_____

_____

Who We Are and Who We Came From

HUSBAND'S PATERNAL GRANDFATHER'S FULL NAME

HUSBAND'S PATERNAL GRANDMOTHER'S FULL NAME

DATE OF MARRIAGE   PLACE OF MARRIAGE

CHILDREN

HUSBAND'S FATHER'S FULL NAME

HUSBAND'S MOTHER'S FULL NAME

DATE OF MARRIAGE   PLACE OF MARRIAGE

CHILDREN

HUSBAND'S MATERNAL GRANDFATHER'S FULL NAME

HUSBAND'S MATERNAL GRANDMOTHER'S FULL NAME

DATE OF MARRIAGE   PLACE OF MARRIAGE

CHILDREN

THE PRECEDING 3 GENERATIONS ON FOLLOWING PAGE ▶

WIFE'S PATERNAL GRANDFATHER'S FULL NAME

WIFE'S PATERNAL GRANDMOTHER'S FULL NAME

DATE OF MARRIAGE   PLACE OF MARRIAGE

CHILDREN

WIFE'S FATHER'S FULL NAME

WIFE'S MOTHER'S FULL NAME

DATE OF MARRIAGE   PLACE OF MARRIAGE

CHILDREN

WIFE'S MATERNAL GRANDFATHER'S FULL NAME

WIFE'S MATERNAL GRANDMOTHER'S FULL NAME

DATE OF MARRIAGE   PLACE OF MARRIAGE

CHILDREN

HUSBAND'S GREAT, GREAT GRANDFATHER'S FULL NAME

HUSBAND'S GREAT, GREAT GRANDMOTHER'S FULL NAME

HUSBAND'S GREAT, GREAT GRANDFATHER'S FULL NAME

HUSBAND'S GREAT, GREAT GRANDMOTHER'S FULL NAME

HUSBAND'S GREAT GRANDFATHER'S FULL NAME

HUSBAND'S GREAT GRANDMOTHER'S FULL NAME

HUSBAND'S GREAT, GREAT GRANDFATHER'S FULL NAME

HUSBAND'S GREAT, GREAT GRANDMOTHER'S FULL NAME

HUSBAND'S GREAT, GREAT GRANDFATHER'S FULL NAME

HUSBAND'S GREAT, GREAT GRANDMOTHER'S FULL NAME

HUSBAND'S GREAT GRANDFATHER'S FULL NAME

HUSBAND'S GREAT GRANDMOTHER'S FULL NAME

HUSBAND'S GREAT, GREAT GRANDFATHER'S FULL NAME

HUSBAND'S GREAT, GREAT GRANDMOTHER'S FULL NAME

HUSBAND'S GREAT, GREAT GRANDFATHER'S FULL NAME

HUSBAND'S GREAT, GREAT GRANDMOTHER'S FULL NAME

HUSBAND'S GREAT GRANDFATHER'S FULL NAME

HUSBAND'S GREAT GRANDMOTHER'S FULL NAME

HUSBAND'S GREAT, GREAT GRANDFATHER'S FULL NAME

HUSBAND'S GREAT, GREAT GRANDMOTHER'S FULL NAME

HUSBAND'S GREAT, GREAT GRANDFATHER'S FULL NAME

HUSBAND'S GREAT, GREAT GRANDMOTHER'S FULL NAME

HUSBAND'S GREAT GRANDFATHER'S FULL NAME

HUSBAND'S GREAT GRANDMOTHER'S FULL NAME

HUSBAND'S GREAT, GREAT GRANDFATHER'S FULL NAME

HUSBAND'S GREAT, GREAT GRANDMOTHER'S FULL NAME

HUSBAND'S GREAT, GREAT GRANDFATHER'S FULL NAME

HUSBAND'S GREAT, GREAT GRANDMOTHER'S FULL NAME

WIFE'S GREAT, GREAT GRANDFATHER'S FULL NAME

WIFE'S GREAT, GREAT GRANDMOTHER'S FULL NAME

WIFE'S GREAT GRANDFATHER'S FULL NAME

WIFE'S GREAT GRANDMOTHER'S FULL NAME

WIFE'S GREAT, GREAT GRANDFATHER'S FULL NAME

WIFE'S GREAT, GREAT GRANDMOTHER'S FULL NAME

WIFE'S GREAT, GREAT GRANDFATHER'S FULL NAME

WIFE'S GREAT, GREAT GRANDMOTHER'S FULL NAME

WIFE'S GREAT GRANDFATHER'S FULL NAME

WIFE'S GREAT GRANDMOTHER'S FULL NAME

WIFE'S GREAT, GREAT GRANDFATHER'S FULL NAME

WIFE'S GREAT, GREAT GRANDMOTHER'S FULL NAME

WIFE'S GREAT, GREAT GRANDFATHER'S FULL NAME

WIFE'S GREAT, GREAT GRANDMOTHER'S FULL NAME

WIFE'S GREAT GRANDFATHER'S FULL NAME

WIFE'S GREAT GRANDMOTHER'S FULL NAME

WIFE'S GREAT, GREAT GRANDFATHER'S FULL NAME

WIFE'S GREAT, GREAT GRANDMOTHER'S FULL NAME

WIFE'S GREAT, GREAT GRANDFATHER'S FULL NAME

WIFE'S GREAT, GREAT GRANDMOTHER'S FULL NAME

WIFE'S GREAT GRANDFATHER'S FULL NAME

WIFE'S GREAT GRANDMOTHER'S FULL NAME

WIFE'S GREAT, GREAT GRANDFATHER'S FULL NAME

WIFE'S GREAT, GREAT GRANDMOTHER'S FULL NAME

WIFE'S GREAT, GREAT GRANDFATHER'S FULL NAME

WIFE'S GREAT, GREAT GRANDMOTHER'S FULL NAME

eat, Great, Great Grandparents

& MRS. _____ NEE _____

& MRS. _____ NEE _____

& MRS. _____ NEE _____

& MRS. _____ NEE _____

& MRS. _____ NEE _____

& MRS. _____ NEE _____

& MRS. _____ NEE _____

& MRS. _____ NEE _____

& MRS. _____ NEE _____

& MRS _____ NEE _____

& MRS. _____ NEE _____

& MRS. _____ NEE _____

& MRS. _____ NEE _____

& MRS. _____ NEE _____

& MRS. _____ NEE _____

& MRS _____ NEE _____

& MRS. _____ NEE _____

& MRS. _____ NEE _____

& MRS. _____ NEE _____

& MRS. _____ NEE _____

& MRS. _____ NEE _____

& MRS. _____ NEE _____

& MRS. _____ NEE _____

, MRS. _____ NEE _____

MRS. _____ NEE _____

MRS. _____ NEE _____

MRS. _____ NEE _____

MRS. _____ NEE _____

MRS. _____ NEE _____

MRS. _____ NEE _____

MRS. _____ NEE _____

MRS. _____ NEE _____

NEE REPRESENTS WIFE'S MAIDEN NAME

The generations preceding the one in the column on the left would have been born about 1800 and of course would be double the number.

Each generation going back in time will be twice the number. If your ancestors landed here in 1600 and you are under 30, you would be the 14th or 15th generation and be descended from over 16,000 people.

For a variety of reasons, families have altered the spelling of the last name or changed it completely. So in looking back and trying to get information from the county, city or town overseas that your family came from, make sure you include as much data as you can get before writing abroad.

Husband's Ancestral Chart

HUSBAND'S FULL NAME

DATE OF BIRTH   PLACE OF BIRTH

DATE OF MARRIAGE   PLACE OF MARRIAGE

DATE OF DEATH   PLACE OF BURIAL

OCCUPATION

SPECIAL INTERESTS

GRANDFATHER'S FULL NAME

DATE OF BIRTH   PLACE OF BIRTH

DATE OF MARRIAGE   PLACE OF MARRIAGE

DATE OF DEATH   PLACE OF BURIAL

OCCUPATION

SPECIAL INTERESTS

FATHER'S FULL NAME

DATE OF BIRTH   PLACE OF BIRTH

DATE OF MARRIAGE   PLACE OF MARRIAGE

DATE OF DEATH   PLACE OF BURIAL

OCCUPATION

SPECIAL INTERESTS

GRANDMOTHER'S FULL NAME

DATE OF BIRTH   PLACE OF BIRTH

DATE OF MARRIAGE   PLACE OF MARRIAGE

DATE OF DEATH   PLACE OF BURIAL

OCCUPATION

SPECIAL INTERESTS

THE PRECEDING 3 GENERATIONS ON FOLLOWING PAGE

GRANDFATHER'S FULL NAME

DATE OF BIRTH   PLACE OF BIRTH

DATE OF MARRIAGE   PLACE OF MARRIAGE

DATE OF DEATH   PLACE OF BURIAL

OCCUPATION

SPECIAL INTERESTS

MOTHER'S FULL NAME

DATE OF BIRTH   PLACE OF BIRTH

DATE OF MARRIAGE   PLACE OF MARRIAGE

DATE OF DEATH   PLACE OF BURIAL

OCCUPATION

SPECIAL INTERESTS

GRANDMOTHER'S FULL NAME

DATE OF BIRTH   PLACE OF BIRTH

DATE OF MARRIAGE   PLACE OF MARRIAGE

DATE OF DEATH   PLACE OF BURIAL

OCCUPATION

SPECIAL INTERESTS

GREAT GRANDFATHER'S FULL NAME

DATE OF BIRTH   PLACE OF BIRTH

OCCUPATION

GREAT GRANDMOTHER'S FULL NAME

DATE OF BIRTH   PLACE OF BIRTH

SPECIAL INTERESTS

GREAT GRANDFATHER'S FULL NAME

DATE OF BIRTH   PLACE OF BIRTH

OCCUPATION

GREAT GRANDMOTHER'S FULL NAME

DATE OF BIRTH   PLACE OF BIRTH

SPECIAL INTERESTS

GREAT GRANDFATHER'S FULL NAME

DATE OF BIRTH   PLACE OF BIRTH

OCCUPATION

GREAT GRANDMOTHER'S FULL NAME

DATE OF BIRTH   PLACE OF BIRTH

SPECIAL INTERESTS

GREAT GRANDFATHER'S FULL NAME

DATE OF BIRTH   PLACE OF BIRTH

OCCUPATION

GREAT GRANDMOTHER'S FULL NAME

DATE OF BIRTH   PLACE OF BIRTH

SPECIAL INTERESTS

GREAT, GREAT GRANDFATHER'S FULL NAME

GREAT, GREAT GRANDMOTHER'S FULL NAME

GREAT, GREAT GRANDFATHER'S FULL NAME

GREAT, GREAT GRANDMOTHER'S FULL NAME

GREAT, GREAT GRANDFATHER'S FULL NAME

GREAT, GREAT GRANDMOTHER'S FULL NAME

GREAT, GREAT GRANDFATHER'S FULL NAME

GREAT, GREAT GRANDMOTHER'S FULL NAME

GREAT, GREAT GRANDFATHER'S FULL NAME

GREAT,, GREAT GRANDMOTHER'S FULL NAME

GREAT, GREAT GRANDFATHER'S FULL NAME

GREAT, GREAT GRANDMOTHER'S FULL NAME

GREAT, GREAT GRANDFATHER'S FULL NAME

GREAT, GREAT GRANDMOTHER'S FULL NAME

GREAT, GREAT GRANDFATHER'S FULL NAME

GREAT, GREAT GRANDMOTHER'S FULL NAME

Great, Great, Great Grandparents

MR. & MRS. _____ NEE _____

MR. & MRS. _____ NEE _____

MR. & MRS. _____ NEE _____

MR. & MRS. _____ NEE _____

MR. & MRS. _____ NEE _____

MR. & MRS. _____ NEE _____

MR. & MRS. _____ NEE _____

MR. & MRS. _____ NEE _____

MR. & MRS. _____ NEE _____

MR. & MRS. _____ NEE _____

MR. & MRS. _____ NEE _____

MR. & MRS. _____ NEE _____

MR. & MRS. _____ NEE _____

MR. & MRS. _____ NEE _____

MR. & MRS. _____ NEE _____

MR. & MRS. _____ NEE _____

MR. & MRS. _____ NEE _____

MR. & MRS. _____ NEE _____

MR. & MRS. _____ NEE _____

MR. & MRS. _____ NEE _____

MR. & MRS. _____ NEE _____

MR. & MRS. _____ NEE _____

MR. & MRS. _____ NEE _____

MR. & MRS. _____ NEE _____

MR. & MRS. _____ NEE _____

MR. & MRS. _____ NEE _____

MR. & MRS. _____ NEE _____

MR. & MRS. _____ NEE _____

MR. & MRS. _____ NEE _____

MR. & MRS. _____ NEE _____

MR. & MRS. _____ NEE _____

MR. & MRS. _____ NEE _____

NEE REPRESENTS WIFE'S MAIDEN NAME

Husband's Family

On this and the next page, fill in all vital statistics on the husband, his brothers and sisters, and their children (nieces and nephews).

**Husband,
his Brothers and Sisters,
and their Children**

	BORN	DIED	SPOUSE
Children			
Children			
Children			
Children			
Children			
Children			
Children			
Children			
Children			

Legal Guardians

(FILL IN NAMES OF LEGAL GUARDIANS FOR ANY CHILD WHERE APPLICABLE, INCLUDING DATES, PLACES AND ANY INFORMATION YOU CONSIDER APPROPRIATE.)

19

Husband's Parents' Family

On this and the following pages, fill in all vital statistics on the husband's parents, their brothers and sisters (aunts and uncles), and their children (cousins).

Husband's Father, his Brothers and Sisters, and their Children

	BORN	DIED	SPOUSE
Children			
Children			
Children			
Children			
Children			
Children			
Children			
Children			
Children			
Children			

Legal Guardians

(FILL IN NAMES OF LEGAL GUARDIANS FOR ANY CHILD WHERE APPLICABLE. INCLUDING DATES. PLACES AND ANY INFORMATION YOU CONSIDER APPROPRIATE.)

Husband's Parents' Family

CONTINUED

**Husband's Mother,
her Brothers and Sisters,
and their Children**

	BORN	DIED	SPOUSE
Children			
Children			
Children			
Children			
Children			
Children			
Children			
Children			
Children			
Children			

Legal Guardians

(FILL IN NAMES OF LEGAL GUARDIANS FOR ANY CHILD WHERE APPLICABLE. INCLUDING DATES. PLACES AND ANY INFORMATION YOU CONSIDER APPROPRIATE.)

Husband's Grandparents— Father's Side

**Grandfather,
his Brothers and Sisters,
and their Children**

	BORN	DIED	SPOUSE
Children			
Children			
Children			
Children			
Children			
Children			
Children			
Children			
Children			

Legal Guardians

(FILL IN NAMES OF LEGAL GUARDIANS FOR ANY CHILD WHERE APPLICABLE INCLUDING DATES. PLACES AND ANY INFORMATION YOU CONSIDER APPROPRIATE.)

Husband's Grandparents— Father's Side

CONTINUED

Grandmother, her Brothers and Sisters, and their Children

	BORN	DIED	SPOUSE
Children			
Children			
Children			
Children			
Children			
Children			
Children			
Children			
Children			

Legal Guardians

(FILL IN NAMES OF LEGAL GUARDIANS FOR ANY CHILD WHERE APPLICABLE, INCLUDING DATES, PLACES AND ANY INFORMATION YOU CONSIDER APPROPRIATE.)

Husband's Grandparents— Mother's Side

**Grandfather,
his Brothers and Sisters,
and their Children**

	BORN	DIED	SPOUSE
Children			
Children			
Children			
Children			
Children			
Children			
Children			
Children			
Children			

Legal Guardians

FILL IN NAMES OF LEGAL GUARDIANS FOR ANY CHILD WHERE APPLICABLE. INCLUDING DATES. PLACES AND ANY INFORMATION YOU CONSIDER APPROPRIATE)

Husband's Grandparents— Mother's Side

CONTINUED

Grandmother, her Brothers and Sisters, and their Children

	BORN	DIED	SPOUSE
Children			
Children			
Children			
Children			
Children			
Children			
Children			
Children			
Children			

Legal Guardians
FILL IN NAMES OF LEGAL GUARDIANS FOR ANY CHILD WHERE APPLICABLE. INCLUDING DATES. PLACES AND ANY INFORMATION YOU CONSIDER APPROPRIATE.)

Husband's Great Grandparents

NAME	BORN	DIED	SPOUSE
_____	_____	_____	_____
Children	_____		
_____	_____	_____	_____
Children	_____		
_____	_____	_____	_____
Children	_____		
_____	_____	_____	_____
Children	_____		
_____	_____	_____	_____
Children	_____		
_____	_____	_____	_____
Children	_____		
_____	_____	_____	_____
Children	_____		
_____	_____	_____	_____
Children	_____		
_____	_____	_____	_____
Children	_____		

Legal Guardians

(FILL IN NAMES OF LEGAL GUARDIANS FOR ANY CHILD WHERE APPLICABLE. INCLUDING DATES, PLACES AND ANY INFORMATION YOU CONSIDER APPROPRIATE.)

Wife's Ancestral Chart

WIFE'S FULL NAME

DATE OF BIRTH   PLACE OF BIRTH

DATE OF MARRIAGE   PLACE OF MARRIAGE

DATE OF DEATH   PLACE OF BURIAL

OCCUPATION

SPECIAL INTERESTS

GRANDFATHER'S FULL NAME

DATE OF BIRTH   PLACE OF BIRTH

DATE OF MARRIAGE   PLACE OF MARRIAGE

DATE OF DEATH   PLACE OF BURIAL

OCCUPATION

SPECIAL INTERESTS

FATHER'S FULL NAME

DATE OF BIRTH   PLACE OF BIRTH

DATE OF MARRIAGE   PLACE OF MARRIAGE

DATE OF DEATH   PLACE OF BURIAL

OCCUPATION

SPECIAL INTERESTS

GRANDMOTHER'S FULL NAME

DATE OF BIRTH   PLACE OF BIRTH

DATE OF MARRIAGE   PLACE OF MARRIAGE

DATE OF DEATH   PLACE OF BURIAL

OCCUPATION

SPECIAL INTERESTS

THE PRECEDING 3 GENERATIONS ON FOLLOWING PAGE

GRANDFATHER'S FULL NAME

DATE OF BIRTH   PLACE OF BIRTH

DATE OF MARRIAGE   PLACE OF MARRIAGE

DATE OF DEATH   PLACE OF BURIAL

OCCUPATION

SPECIAL INTERESTS

MOTHER'S FULL NAME

DATE OF BIRTH   PLACE OF BIRTH

DATE OF MARRIAGE   PLACE OF MARRIAGE

DATE OF DEATH   PLACE OF BURIAL

OCCUPATION

SPECIAL INTERESTS

GRANDMOTHER'S FULL NAME

DATE OF BIRTH   PLACE OF BIRTH

DATE OF MARRIAGE   PLACE OF MARRIAGE

DATE OF DEATH   PLACE OF BURIAL

OCCUPATION

SPECIAL INTERESTS

35

GREAT GRANDFATHER'S FULL NAME

DATE OF BIRTH   PLACE OF BIRTH

OCCUPATION

GREAT GRANDMOTHER'S FULL NAME

DATE OF BIRTH   PLACE OF BIRTH

SPECIAL INTERESTS

GREAT GRANDFATHER'S FULL NAME

DATE OF BIRTH   PLACE OF BIRTH

OCCUPATION

GREAT GRANDMOTHER'S FULL NAME

DATE OF BIRTH   PLACE OF BIRTH

SPECIAL INTERESTS

GREAT GRANDFATHER'S FULL NAME

DATE OF BIRTH   PLACE OF BIRTH

OCCUPATION

GREAT GRANDMOTHER'S FULL NAME

DATE OF BIRTH   PLACE OF BIRTH

SPECIAL INTERESTS

GREAT GRANDFATHER'S FULL NAME

DATE OF BIRTH   PLACE OF BIRTH

OCCUPATION

GREAT GRANDMOTHER'S FULL NAME

DATE OF BIRTH   PLACE OF BIRTH

SPECIAL INTERESTS

GREAT, GREAT GRANDFATHER'S FULL NAME

GREAT, GREAT GRANDMOTHER'S FULL NAME

GREAT, GREAT GRANDFATHER'S FULL NAME

GREAT, GREAT GRANDMOTHER'S FULL NAME

GREAT, GREAT GRANDFATHER'S FULL NAME

GREAT, GREAT GRANDMOTHER'S FULL NAME

GREAT, GREAT GRANDFATHER'S FULL NAME

GREAT, GREAT GRANDMOTHER'S FULL NAME

GREAT, GREAT GRANDFATHER'S FULL NAME

GREAT, GREAT GRANDMOTHER'S FULL NAME

GREAT, GREAT GRANDFATHER'S FULL NAME

GREAT, GREAT GRANDMOTHER'S FULL NAME

GREAT, GREAT GRANDFATHER'S FULL NAME

GREAT, GREAT GRANDMOTHER'S FULL NAME

GREAT, GREAT GRANDFATHER'S FULL NAME

GREAT, GREAT GRANDMOTHER'S FULL NAME

Great, Great, Great Grandparents

MR. & MRS. ————————————————————— NEE ———————————————

MR. & MRS. ————————————————————— NEE ———————————————

MR. & MRS. ————————————————————— NEE ———————————————

MR. & MRS. ————————————————————— NEE ———————————————

MR. & MRS. ————————————————————— NEE ———————————————

MR. & MRS. ————————————————————— NEE ———————————————

MR. & MRS. ————————————————————— NEE ———————————————

MR. & MRS. ————————————————————— NEE ———————————————

MR. & MRS. ————————————————————— NEE ———————————————

MR. & MRS. ————————————————————— NEE ———————————————

MR. & MRS. ————————————————————— NEE ———————————————

MR. & MRS. ————————————————————— NEE ———————————————

MR. & MRS. ————————————————————— NEE ———————————————

MR. & MRS. ————————————————————— NEE ———————————————

MR. & MRS. ————————————————————— NEE ———————————————

MR. & MRS. ————————————————————— NEE ———————————————

MR. & MRS. ————————————————————— NEE ———————————————

MR. & MRS. ————————————————————— NEE ———————————————

MR. & MRS. ————————————————————— NEE ———————————————

MR. & MRS. ————————————————————— NEE ———————————————

MR. & MRS. ————————————————————— NEE ———————————————

MR. & MRS. ————————————————————— NEE ———————————————

MR. & MRS. ————————————————————— NEE ———————————————

MR. & MRS. ————————————————————— NEE ———————————————

MR. & MRS. ————————————————————— NEE ———————————————

MR. & MRS. ————————————————————— NEE ———————————————

MR. & MRS. ————————————————————— NEE ———————————————

MR. & MRS. ————————————————————— NEE ———————————————

MR. & MRS. ————————————————————— NEE ———————————————

MR. & MRS. ————————————————————— NEE ———————————————

MR. & MRS. ————————————————————— NEE ———————————————

MR. & MRS. ————————————————————— NEE ———————————————

NEE REPRESENTS WIFE'S MAIDEN NAME

Wife's Family

On this and the next page, fill in all vital statistics on the wife, her brothers and sisters, and their children (nieces and nephews).

Wife, her Brothers and Sisters, and their Children	BORN	DIED	SPOUSE
_____	_____	_____	_____
Children _____	_____	_____	_____
_____	_____	_____	_____
Children _____	_____	_____	_____
_____	_____	_____	_____
Children _____	_____	_____	_____
_____	_____	_____	_____
Children _____	_____	_____	_____
_____	_____	_____	_____
Children _____	_____	_____	_____
_____	_____	_____	_____
Children _____	_____	_____	_____
_____	_____	_____	_____
Children _____	_____	_____	_____
_____	_____	_____	_____
Children _____	_____	_____	_____
_____	_____	_____	_____
Children _____	_____	_____	_____
_____	_____	_____	_____
Children _____	_____	_____	_____

Legal Guardians

(FILL IN NAMES OF LEGAL GUARDIANS FOR ANY CHILD WHERE APPLICABLE, INCLUDING DATES, PLACES AND ANY INFORMATION YOU CONSIDER APPROPRIATE.)

Wife's Parents' Family

On this and the following pages, fill in all vital statistics on the wife's parents, their brothers and sisters (aunts and uncles), and their children (cousins).

**Wife's Father,
his Brothers and Sisters,
and their Children**

	BORN	DIED	SPOUSE
Children			
Children			
Children			
Children			
Children			
Children			
Children			
Children			
Children			

Legal Guardians

(FILL IN NAMES OF LEGAL GUARDIANS FOR ANY CHILD WHERE APPLICABLE. INCLUDING DATES. PLACES AND ANY INFORMATION YOU CONSIDER APPROPRIATE.)

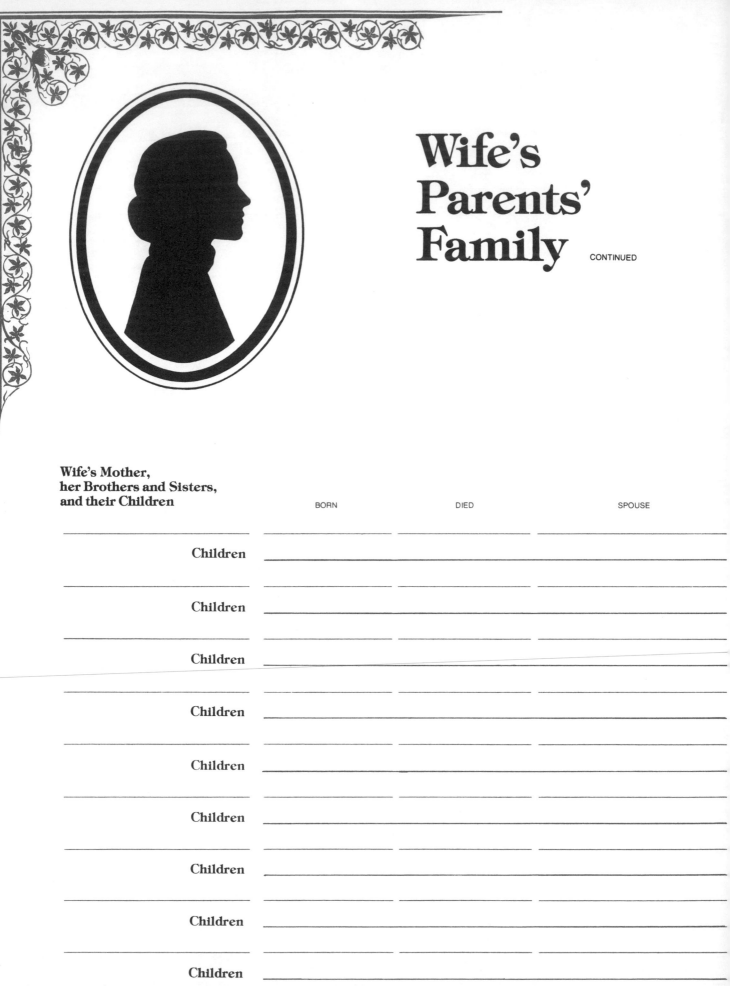

Wife's Parents' Family CONTINUED

**Wife's Mother,
her Brothers and Sisters,
and their Children**

	BORN	DIED	SPOUSE
Children			
Children			
Children			
Children			
Children			
Children			
Children			
Children			
Children			

Legal Guardians

(FILL IN NAMES OF LEGAL GUARDIANS FOR ANY CHILD WHERE APPLICABLE. INCLUDING DATES. PLACES AND ANY INFORMATION YOU CONSIDER APPROPRIATE.)

Wife's Grandparents— Father's Side

**Grandfather,
his Brothers and Sisters,
and their Children**

	BORN	DIED	SPOUSE
Children			
Children			
Children			
Children			
Children			
Children			
Children			
Children			
Children			

Legal Guardians

(FILL IN NAMES OF LEGAL GUARDIANS FOR ANY CHILD WHERE APPLICABLE. INCLUDING DATES. PLACES AND ANY INFORMATION YOU CONSIDER APPROPRIATE.)

45

Wife's Grandparents— Father's Side

CONTINUED

**Grandmother,
her Brothers and Sisters,
and their Children**

	BORN	DIED	SPOUSE
Children			
Children			
Children			
Children			
Children			
Children			
Children			
Children			
Children			

Legal Guardians
(FILL IN NAMES OF LEGAL GUARDIANS FOR ANY CHILD WHERE APPLICABLE. INCLUDING DATES. PLACES AND ANY INFORMATION YOU CONSIDER APPROPRIATE.)

Wife's Grandparents— Mother's Side

**Grandfather,
his Brothers and Sisters,
and their Children**

	BORN	DIED	SPOUSE
Children			
Children			
Children			
Children			
Children			
Children			
Children			
Children			
Children			

Legal Guardians

Wife's Grandparents— Mother's Side

CONTINUED

Grandmother, her Brothers and Sisters, and their Children

	BORN	DIED	SPOUSE
Children			
Children			
Children			
Children			
Children			
Children			
Children			
Children			
Children			

Legal Guardians

(FILL IN NAMES OF LEGAL GUARDIANS FOR ANY CHILD WHERE APPLICABLE. INCLUDING DATES. PLACES AND ANY INFORMATION YOU CONSIDER APPROPRIATE.)

51

Wife's Great Grandparents

NAME	BORN	DIED	SPOUSE
_____	_____	_____	_____
Children	_____		
_____	_____	_____	_____
Children	_____		
_____	_____	_____	_____
Children	_____		
_____	_____	_____	_____
Children	_____		
_____	_____	_____	_____
Children	_____		
_____	_____	_____	_____
Children	_____		
_____	_____	_____	_____
Children	_____		
_____	_____	_____	_____
Children	_____		
_____	_____	_____	_____
Children	_____		

Legal Guardians
(FILL IN NAMES OF LEGAL GUARDIANS FOR ANY CHILD WHERE APPLICABLE. INCLUDING DATES, PLACES AND ANY INFORMATION YOU CONSIDER APPROPRIATE.)

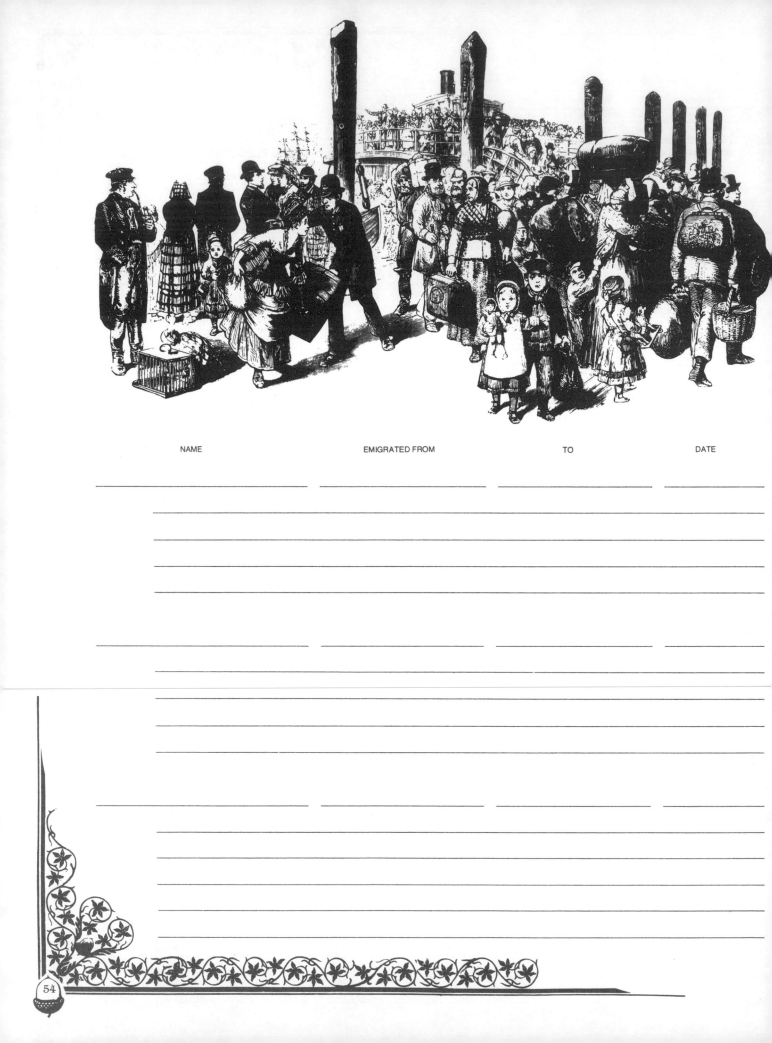

NAME	EMIGRATED FROM	TO	DATE

Citizenship Record

In the space below fill in the countries your family came from along with any other information about that place you have or can get. Also put in when the family emigrated, where they landed and how your branch settled where it is now.

NAME	EMIGRATED FROM	TO	DATE

Citizenship
Record CONTINUED

Weddings

_____
_____
_____
_____
_____
_____
_____
_____

NAMES	DATE	PLACE

NAMES	DATE	PLACE

Weddings CONTINUED

_____
_____
_____
_____
_____
_____
_____
_____
_____
_____
_____
_____
_____
_____
_____
_____
_____
_____
_____
_____
_____
_____
_____
_____
_____
_____
_____

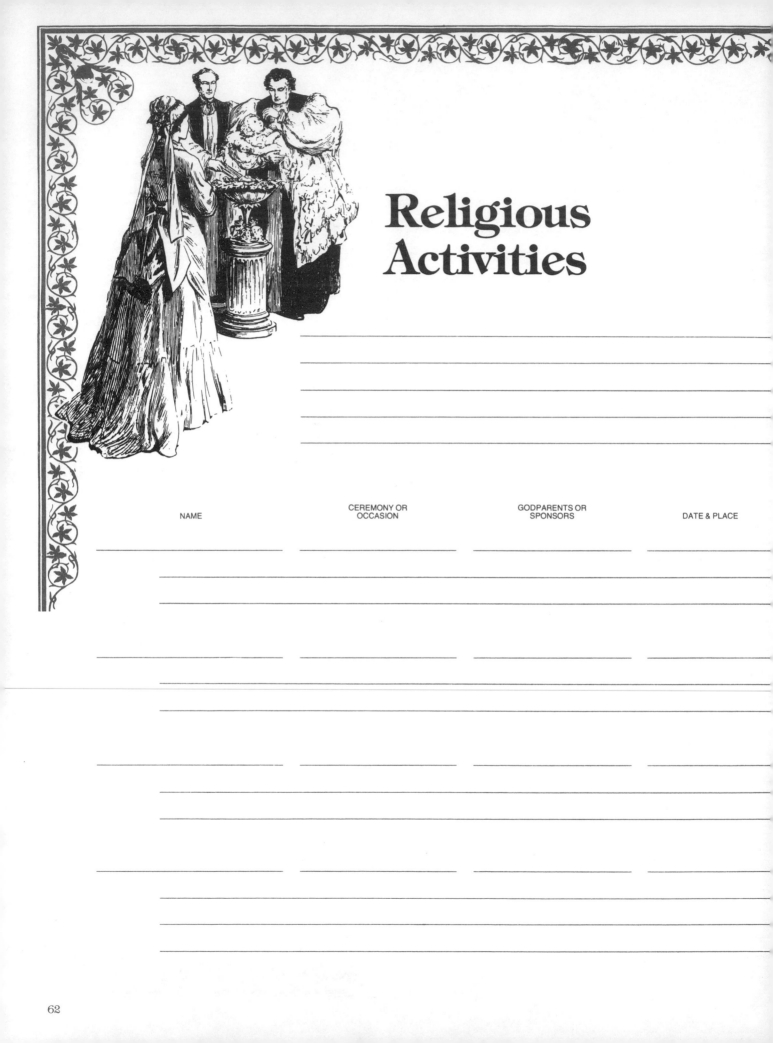

Religious Activities

NAME	CEREMONY OR OCCASION	GODPARENTS OR SPONSORS	DATE & PLACE

NAME	CEREMONY OR OCCASION	GODPARENTS OR SPONSORS	DATE & PLACE

Religious Activities CONTINUED

_____
_____
_____
_____
_____
_____
_____
_____
_____
_____
_____
_____
_____
_____
_____
_____
_____
_____
_____
_____
_____
_____
_____
_____

Our Places of Worship

_____
_____
_____
_____
_____
_____
_____
_____
_____
_____
_____
_____
_____
_____
_____
_____
_____
_____
_____
_____
_____
_____
_____
_____
_____
_____
_____
_____
_____
_____

In Memoriam

Here you may record names of those who have died about whom you have special memories. You may write stories you have heard or your own personal thoughts.

In Memoriam

CONTINUED

Our Homes

Street Address _____

City _____ State _____

Date of Purchase _____ Resided from _____ to _____

_____
_____
_____
_____
_____
_____
_____
_____

Street Address _____

City _____ State _____

Date of Purchase _____ Resided from _____ to _____

_____
_____
_____
_____
_____
_____
_____

Street Address _____

City _____ **State** _____

Date of Purchase _____ **Resided from** _____ **to** _____

_____

_____

_____

_____

_____

_____

Street Address _____

City _____ **State** _____

Date of Purchase _____ **Resided from** _____ **to** _____

_____

_____

_____

_____

_____

_____

Street Address _____

City _____ **State** _____

Date of Purchase _____ **Resided from** _____ **to** _____

_____

_____

_____

_____

_____

_____

Street Address ———

City ————————————————————————————— State —————————————————————

Date of Purchase ————————————— Resided from ————————— to —————————

——

——

——

——

——

——

——

Street Address ———

City ————————————————————————————— State —————————————————————

Date of Purchase ————————————— Resided from ————————— to —————————

——

——

——

——

——

——

——

Street Address ———

City ————————————————————————————— State —————————————————————

Date of Purchase ————————————— Resided from ————————— to —————————

——

——

——

——

——

Where Our Ancestors Have Lived

Schools

NAME	SCHOOL, COLLEGE OR UNIVERSITY	DATES OF ATTENDANCE	CERTIFICATE OR DEGREE

and Graduations

Schools and Graduations CONTINUED

Important School Achievements—Fine Arts, Athletics and Others

NAME	ACHIEVEMENT	DATE	SCHOOL

Clubs and Organizations

NAME	ORGANIZATION	ACTIVITY, AWARD, OFFICE HELD	DATE

Fill in names of family members and their clubs
and organizations, including offices held and any
other interesting information about the person or
the organization.

Companies
We Have
Worked
For or
Owned

You may record here employment histories and
businesses started by any member of your family,
including when and where a business was begun,
and its success or failure and why.

Companies We Have Worked For or Owned

CONTINUED

Social Security Numbers

Military Service Records

NAME

SERVICE NUMBER :

JOB CLASSIFICATION :

ENLISTED OR INDUCTED:

MONTH: DAY: YEAR: AT AGE

BRANCH OF SERVICE GRADE

TRAINING CAMPS SERVICE SCHOOLS ATTENDED:

DIVISION: REGIMENT: DEPARTMENT OR SHIP: DATES

COMPANY: TRANSFERRED:

PROMOTIONS AND DATES:

OVERSEAS SERVICE: DEPARTURE DATE PORT: RETURN DATE PORT:

BATTLES, ENGAGEMENTS, SKIRMISHES, EXPEDITIONS: COMMANDING OFFICERS: CITATIONS:

WOUNDS RECEIVED IN SERVICE; SICKNESS OR HOSPITALIZATION:

IMPORTANT LEAVES OR FURLOUGHS:

DISCHARGED AT OR SEPARATION.

NAME _____ SERVICE NUMBER: _____ JOB CLASSIFICATION: _____

ENLISTED OR INDUCTED: _____ MONTH: _____ DAY: _____ YEAR: _____ AT AGE _____

BRANCH OF SERVICE _____ GRADE _____

TRAINING CAMPS _____ SERVICE SCHOOLS ATTENDED: _____

_____

_____

_____

DIVISION: _____ REGIMENT: _____ DEPARTMENT OR SHIP: _____ DATES _____

COMPANY: _____ TRANSFERRED: _____

_____

PROMOTIONS AND DATES: _____

_____

_____

_____

OVERSEAS SERVICE: _____ DEPARTURE DATE _____ PORT: _____ RETURN DATE _____ PORT: _____

_____

_____

_____

_____

BATTLES, ENGAGEMENTS, SKIRMISHES, EXPEDITIONS: _____ COMMANDING OFFICERS: _____ CITATIONS: _____

_____

_____

_____

_____

WOUNDS RECEIVED IN SERVICE; SICKNESS OR HOSPITALIZATION: _____

_____

_____

IMPORTANT LEAVES OR FURLOUGHS: _____

_____

DISCHARGED AT. OR SEPARATION. _____

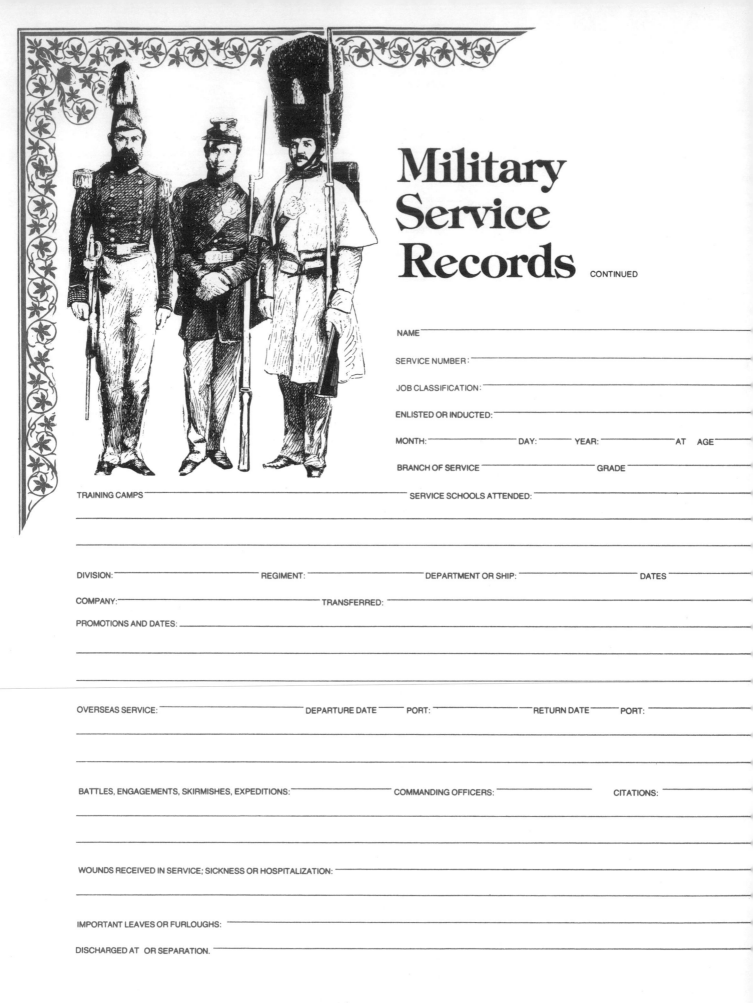

Military Service Records CONTINUED

NAME

SERVICE NUMBER :

JOB CLASSIFICATION :

ENLISTED OR INDUCTED:

MONTH: DAY: YEAR: AT AGE

BRANCH OF SERVICE GRADE

TRAINING CAMPS SERVICE SCHOOLS ATTENDED:

DIVISION: REGIMENT: DEPARTMENT OR SHIP: DATES

COMPANY: TRANSFERRED:

PROMOTIONS AND DATES:

OVERSEAS SERVICE: DEPARTURE DATE PORT: RETURN DATE PORT:

BATTLES, ENGAGEMENTS, SKIRMISHES, EXPEDITIONS: COMMANDING OFFICERS: CITATIONS:

WOUNDS RECEIVED IN SERVICE; SICKNESS OR HOSPITALIZATION:

IMPORTANT LEAVES OR FURLOUGHS:

DISCHARGED AT OR SEPARATION.

NAME _____ SERVICE NUMBER: _____ JOB CLASSIFICATION: _____

ENLISTED OR INDUCTED: _____ MONTH: _____ DAY: _____ YEAR: _____ AT AGE _____

BRANCH OF SERVICE _____ GRADE _____

TRAINING CAMPS _____ SERVICE SCHOOLS ATTENDED: _____

_____

_____

_____

DIVISION: _____ REGIMENT: _____ DEPARTMENT OR SHIP: _____ DATES _____

COMPANY: _____ TRANSFERRED: _____

_____

PROMOTIONS AND DATES: _____

_____

_____

_____

OVERSEAS SERVICE: _____ DEPARTURE DATE _____ PORT: _____ RETURN DATE _____ PORT: _____

_____

_____

_____

_____

BATTLES, ENGAGEMENTS, SKIRMISHES, EXPEDITIONS: _____ COMMANDING OFFICERS: _____ CITATIONS: _____

_____

_____

_____

WOUNDS RECEIVED IN SERVICE; SICKNESS OR HOSPITALIZATION: _____

_____

_____

IMPORTANT LEAVES OR FURLOUGHS: _____

_____

DISCHARGED AT OR SEPARATION. _____

87

Military Service Records CONTINUED

NAME

SERVICE NUMBER :

JOB CLASSIFICATION :

ENLISTED OR INDUCTED:

MONTH: DAY: YEAR: AT AGE

BRANCH OF SERVICE GRADE

TRAINING CAMPS SERVICE SCHOOLS ATTENDED:

DIVISION: REGIMENT: DEPARTMENT OR SHIP: DATES

COMPANY: TRANSFERRED:

PROMOTIONS AND DATES:

OVERSEAS SERVICE: DEPARTURE DATE PORT: RETURN DATE PORT:

BATTLES, ENGAGEMENTS, SKIRMISHES, EXPEDITIONS: COMMANDING OFFICERS: CITATIONS:

WOUNDS RECEIVED IN SERVICE; SICKNESS OR HOSPITALIZATION:

IMPORTANT LEAVES OR FURLOUGHS:

DISCHARGED AT OR SEPARATION.

NAME _____ SERVICE NUMBER: _____ JOB CLASSIFICATION: _____

ENLISTED OR INDUCTED: _____ MONTH: _____ DAY: _____ YEAR: _____ AT AGE _____

BRANCH OF SERVICE _____ GRADE _____

TRAINING CAMPS _____ SERVICE SCHOOLS ATTENDED: _____

_____

_____

_____

DIVISION: _____ REGIMENT: _____ DEPARTMENT OR SHIP: _____ DATES _____

COMPANY: _____ TRANSFERRED: _____

_____

PROMOTIONS AND DATES: _____

_____

_____

_____

OVERSEAS SERVICE: _____ DEPARTURE DATE _____ PORT: _____ RETURN DATE _____ PORT: _____

_____

_____

_____

_____

_____

BATTLES, ENGAGEMENTS, SKIRMISHES, EXPEDITIONS: _____ COMMANDING OFFICERS: _____ CITATIONS: _____

_____

_____

_____

_____

WOUNDS RECEIVED IN SERVICE; SICKNESS OR HOSPITALIZATION: _____

_____

_____

IMPORTANT LEAVES OR FURLOUGHS: _____

_____

DISCHARGED AT OR SEPARATION. _____

Military Service Records CONTINUED

NAME

SERVICE NUMBER:

JOB CLASSIFICATION:

ENLISTED OR INDUCTED:

MONTH: DAY: YEAR: AT AGE

BRANCH OF SERVICE GRADE

TRAINING CAMPS SERVICE SCHOOLS ATTENDED:

DIVISION: REGIMENT: DEPARTMENT OR SHIP: DATES

COMPANY: TRANSFERRED:

PROMOTIONS AND DATES:

OVERSEAS SERVICE: DEPARTURE DATE PORT: RETURN DATE PORT:

BATTLES, ENGAGEMENTS, SKIRMISHES, EXPEDITIONS: COMMANDING OFFICERS: CITATIONS:

WOUNDS RECEIVED IN SERVICE; SICKNESS OR HOSPITALIZATION:

IMPORTANT LEAVES OR FURLOUGHS:

DISCHARGED AT OR SEPARATION.

NAME _____ SERVICE NUMBER: _____ JOB CLASSIFICATION: _____

ENLISTED OR INDUCTED: _____ MONTH: _____ DAY: _____ YEAR: _____ AT AGE _____

BRANCH OF SERVICE _____ GRADE _____

TRAINING CAMPS _____ SERVICE SCHOOLS ATTENDED: _____

_____

_____

_____

DIVISION: _____ REGIMENT: _____ DEPARTMENT OR SHIP: _____ DATES _____

COMPANY: _____ TRANSFERRED: _____

_____

PROMOTIONS AND DATES: _____

_____

_____

_____

OVERSEAS SERVICE: _____ DEPARTURE DATE _____ PORT: _____ RETURN DATE _____ PORT: _____

_____

_____

_____

_____

BATTLES, ENGAGEMENTS, SKIRMISHES, EXPEDITIONS: _____ COMMANDING OFFICERS: _____ CITATIONS: _____

_____

_____

_____

_____

WOUNDS RECEIVED IN SERVICE; SICKNESS OR HOSPITALIZATION: _____

_____

_____

IMPORTANT LEAVES OR FURLOUGHS: _____

_____

DISCHARGED AT. OR SEPARATION. _____

Special Friends

Everyone has a best friend who sometimes seems a part of the family. Certainly they make up some big parts of your life, so including them in a family record book seems appropriate. Don't forget to include dates, addresses and some of those things that make these people so special.

Our Pets

The chances are millions to one that you have a pet elephant but more than likely you have a dog, cat, turtle or fish. Animals, like good friends, seem to become part of the family and play a part in our daily lives. Because they are integrated into the 'family,' remembering them will recall fond memories.

OWNER	PET'S NAME	TYPE OF PET	DATES OF OWNERSHIP

Family Automobiles

OWNER	MAKE, MODEL, YEAR	COLOR	DATES OF OWNERSHIP

Americans have always been a people on the move and ever since Henry Ford started to mass produce cars they have been a part of almost every family's life. Every auto you have owned or will own has a special place in your life and remembering them will bring back lots of memories.

Favorite Things

HIS—HERS

Songs—Records

Books—Shows
Places—Recipes, etc.

CHILDREN

Songs—Records
Stories—Toys
Places—Pastimes, etc.

Collections and Heirlooms

Include here special collections of various family members—what they are, when begun, how much collected, etc. List all heirlooms, including original owner and how items were passed from generation to generation. In short, record anything of interest to you that will also be of interest to others who read about your family.

_____
_____
_____
_____
_____
_____
_____
_____
_____
_____
_____
_____
_____
_____
_____
_____
_____
_____
_____
_____
_____

Collections and Heirlooms

CONTINUED

Favorite Family Sports

FAMILY OR INDIVIDUAL'S NAME	SPORT, TEAM, CLUB	SPECIAL ACHIEVEMENT

Favorite Family Sports CONTINUED

From woodcarving and quilt making to rebuilding old cars and raising exotic plants, many families have individuals who pursue a wide variety of interesting hobbies. Here is space to record those individuals and their pastimes and any fascinating pieces of information about how they started and why and whether anyone else followed in their footsteps.

Favorite Family Hobbies

Favorite Family Hobbies CONTINUED

_____
_____
_____
_____
_____
_____
_____
_____
_____
_____
_____
_____
_____
_____
_____
_____
_____
_____
_____
_____
_____
_____

Family Vacations

Getting away from it all seems to keep us going through the rest of the year so entering some of the places you go to, who was there, and what happened can help bring back some of that fun. Some vacations are not so much where you went as what you did or who you met, so by recording this you have the chance, in the future, to look back and smile or cry.

Family Reunions

Remembering who was there and at what occasion is a lot easier if you record it here. In years to come this kind of information will conjure up the event all over again for you. No matter whether it was your fifth high school class reunion or the family's Fiftieth Wedding Anniversary.

who was there

Family Reunions

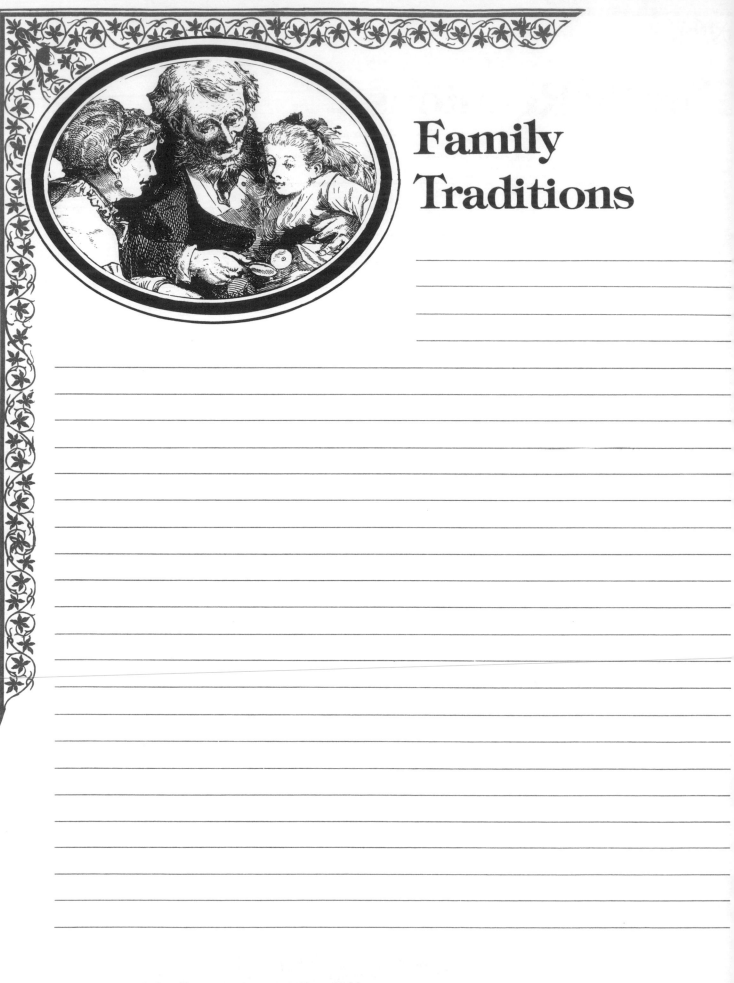

Family Traditions

Events
to Remember

Here you may record information about events (other than such things as reunions, trips, and club activities) that you may want to recall years from now. Include family "firsts" and unique achievements—winning a special prize, meeting a famed personality, or witnessing an outstanding event.

_____

_____

_____

_____

_____

_____

_____

_____

_____

_____

_____

_____

_____

_____

_____

_____

_____

_____

_____

_____

_____

_____

_____

_____

_____

Events to Remember

Oral Family History

From survivors and participants in wars to
migrations from other countries, each family has
stories no one has ever written down. Here is
space to do so to record forever what will be lost
if it remains "oral history."

_____

_____

_____

_____

_____

_____

_____

_____

_____

_____

_____

_____

_____

_____

_____

_____

_____

_____

_____

_____

_____

_____

_____

_____

_____

_____

_____

_____

Oral
Family
History

CONTINUED

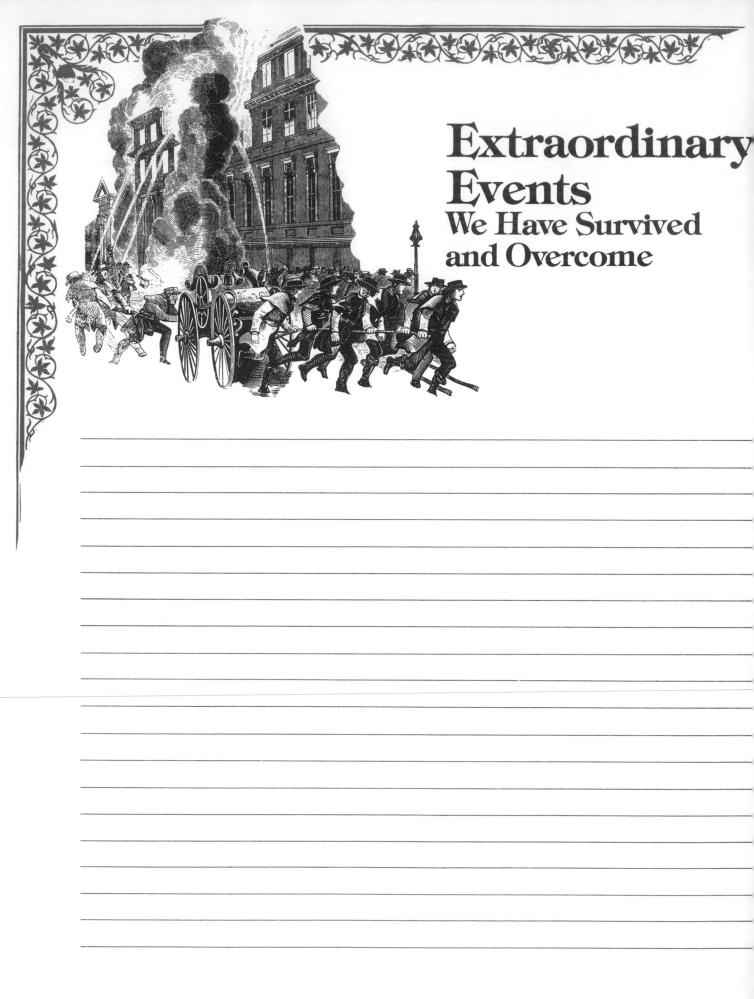

Extraordinary
Events
We Have Survived
and Overcome

Into each family come those unforeseen events.
Many have survived natural disasters (floods,
tornados) and many times families were forced
to move or lives were altered for the better as a
result. Here is space for you to record whatever
you feel is appropriate in relation to your own
family's experiences.

Illnesses

NAME	ILLNESS, OPERATION	HOSPITAL, DOCTOR	DATE

HIS _____

Height _____

Weight _____

Hair Color _____

Color of Eyes _____

Suit Size _____

Shirt Size _____

Waist _____

Shoe Size _____

Hat Size _____

Ring Size _____

Other Sizes _____

_____

_____

_____

_____

_____

_____

Color Preference _____

_____

_____

_____

Toiletries Preference _____

_____

_____

Vital Statistics

Space is provided on these pages for vital statistics. Fill in with as much detail as you care to note.

_____

_____

_____

_____

HERS _____

Height _____

Weight _____

Hair Color _____

Color of Eyes _____

Blouse Size _____

Dress Size _____

Shoe Size _____

Ring Size _____

Other Sizes _____

_____

_____

_____

_____

_____

_____

_____

_____

_____

Color Preference _____

_____

_____

_____

Perfume & Toiletries Preference _____

_____

_____

Vital Statistics _{CONTINUED}

CHILDREN	Height	Weight	Hair Color	Color of

Color Preference _____

Size	Blouse Size					
s Size	Shirt Size	Shoe Size	Hat Size	Ring Size	Other Sizes	

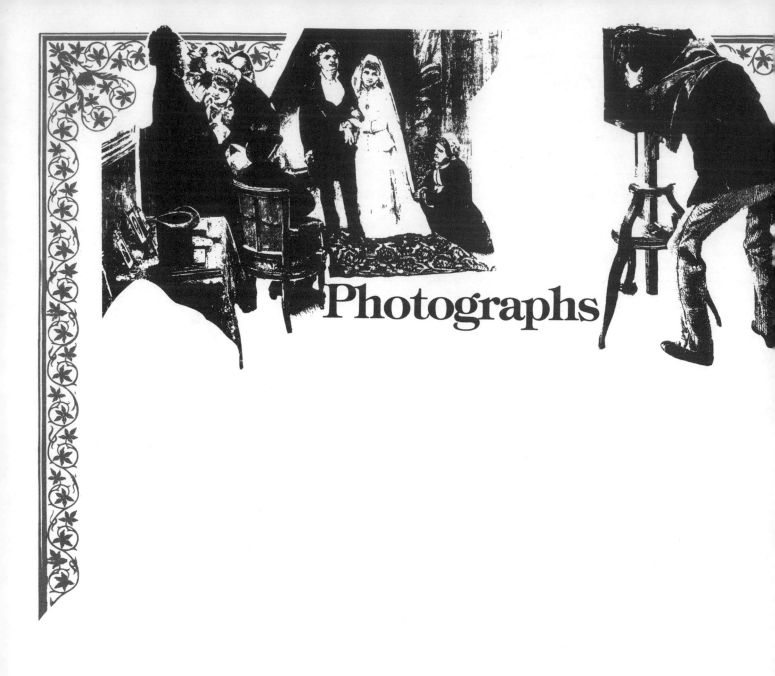

Photographs

Pictures do their own story telling and in years to come a lot can be learned from this kind of record. You and future generations will be able to look back and see a member of the family in his or her own time and place. (You may also want to include favorite clippings, mementos, or documents.)

Photographs

CONTINUED

Photographs

CONTINUED

Genealogy Research

All of us know something about our living relatives. We enjoy telling stories about their achievements and exploits, and we certainly have a fondness for the endearing characters which are in most families. Yet our knowledge of our families often does not go beyond those members we actually know. Few of us have been lucky enough to have known our greatgrandparents for example. This shows us that one of the most common ways of learning about ourselves is by word of mouth; the so-called oral tradition. Thus, if you want to begin finding out more about your family the place to start is with your relatives. Ask them if they can provide you with the birth dates, places of residence and dates of death of those who you do not know, such as your greatgrandparents. Do this as far as it is possible to trace them. Once you have reached this point you will often discover the great treasures of information available in family bibles, picture albums, old letters, diaries and account books. Your ancestors often kept better records than you think!

Once you have names, dates and places you can consult town records. Securing birth certificates, marriage licenses, death certificates, wills and land deeds will give you additional names you will want and need. Don't be disappointed if some of these public records are not available. You can always check your public library. Some of the subjects you can look up at the library are clans, deeds, epitaphs, estates, marriage licenses, nobility, parish registers, peerage and precedence. Also don't forget to ask the librarian for additional sources of genealogical information. If the books listed in the card catalogue should not be in the stacks, your librarian can easily send for them.

Another place to check is your state genealogical association or historical society. Each state has its own organization with qualified people who can be very helpful in local matters. These associations also often publish their own periodicals which you might like to look into. The Daughters of the American Revolution in your area may also be able to furnish you with further information. Sometimes they too publish interesting pamphlets on the subject.

The next step in your search is to contact the National Archives, which is the central United States depository for records, located in Washington, D.C., to find out which of their eleven regional branches is nearest to you. The Archives contain many different kinds of records which will be helpful to you. The Census Records, from 1790 to date, are kept here. They give information such as the name of each member of a family, his age, occupation and place of birth. Also available are records of military service, pensions and land grants. Since we are a nation of immigrants you may find here the names of the first members of your family who came to America, as well as the name of the ship that brought them, the date of arrival, the port of entry and the date of naturalization. For other such information one should consult the United States Immigration and Naturalization office.